JOURNEY INTO SPACE

Autumn
Publishing

Published in 2022
First published in the UK by Autumn Publishing
An imprint of Igloo Books Ltd
Cottage Farm, NN6 0BJ, UK
Owned by Bonnier Books
Sveavägen 56, Stockholm, Sweden
www.autumnpublishing.co.uk

0522 005
6 8 10 9 7 5
ISBN 978-1-78810-997-0

Illustrated by Nanette Regan
Written by Marnie Willow

Designed by Chris Stanley
Edited by Helen Catt

Printed and manufactured in China

JOURNEY INTO SPACE

Autumn
Publishing

Max and Rosie had been given another important mission. They went to the lab at the Space Centre to find out more.

"It says here we're to fly into space in a rocket to reach the International Space Station," said Rosie, reading the instructions.

Before they could go into space, Rosie and Max had to do a lot of training.

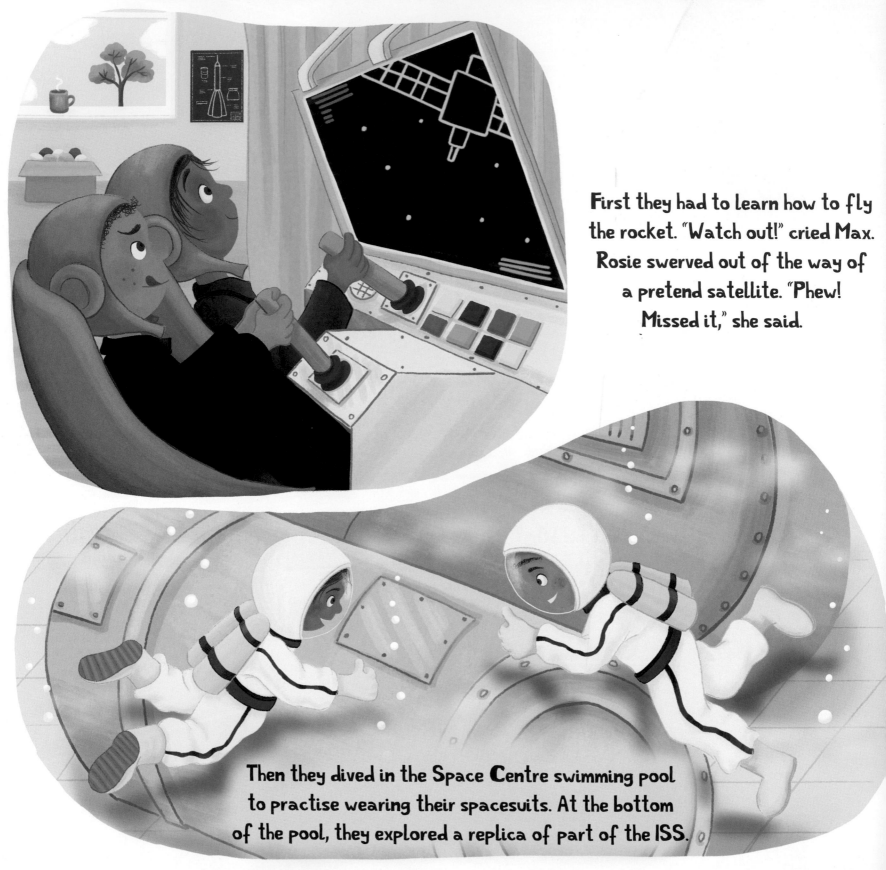

First they had to learn how to fly the rocket. "Watch out!" cried Max. Rosie swerved out of the way of a pretend satellite. "Phew! Missed it," she said.

Then they dived in the Space Centre swimming pool to practise wearing their spacesuits. At the bottom of the pool, they explored a replica of part of the ISS.

Finally, they flew in a plane that climbed thousands of metres high, then suddenly dived down.

As the plane went into freefall, Max and Rosie became **weightless,** just like they would in space. "I think I'm going to like zero-gravity!" chuckled Max, as he did a somersault.

After all their training, Max and Rosie were finally ready to go into space.

At last, when the fuel tanks were full and all the last checks had been made, the engines started to **rumble**...

...10 9 8 7 6 5

4 3 2 1

"LIFT-OFF!"

shouted Max and Rosie together.

The booster engines **roared!**
Max and Rosie clung on tightly as the
rocket **blasted** up through
the Earth's atmosphere.

THUNK!

"What was that?" asked Rosie. Max peered out through the porthole.

"Don't worry," he said. "It's just the boosters dropping away. We've used up the fuel that we needed for lift-off, so there's no point in carrying extra weight."

CLUNK!

"There goes the core of the rocket," said Max, as they continued whizzing up and up.

Rosie and Max looked through the porthole at the Earth spinning slowly on its axis far below.

Rosie took the controls and carefully navigated towards the International Space Station.

"This is the tricky bit," she said. She steered the capsule slowly towards the docking module on the ISS, inching closer and closer until...

... CLANG!

The capsule clicked into place, linking safely with the docking module.

Rosie and Max undid their seatbelts, opened the hatch, and floated into the ISS.

"Welcome aboard!" cheered the astronauts. "My name's Alice," said one of them. "Come and look around!"

"These are the sleeping pods," said Alice, pointing to a snoozing astronaut who was strapped to the wall.

"Here's the treadmill. Without gravity, our muscles get weak easily, so we exercise for two hours every day."

"And here's the canteen." Alice gave them sachets of space food. Max squeezed a sachet and a round drop of liquid spun slowly upwards.

"Wow!"

he cried, and caught the droplet in his mouth.

"And finally this is the lab where we do our experiments," said Alice.

"We're using the seedlings you brought to find out how things grow in space.
They'll help us work out how to make clean air and water here in orbit."
"Wow," whispered Rosie. "That's a big job for such tiny seedlings."

Suddenly, an alarm **blared** and red lights started flashing.

BEEP!
BEEP!

"Oh no! A micrometeorite has **punctured** one of the solar panels," said Alice. "**C**an you two fix it?"
"Sure!" said Max and Rosie, putting on their spacesuits.

The two explorers went out through the airlock and carefully made their way towards the solar panels. They unscrewed the damaged section and replaced it with a shiny new panel.

"Oops!" said Rosie, as she put the drill down and it floated away. "Good thing it's attached to my spacesuit!"

When they got back inside the Station, it was time for Max and Rosie to head back to Earth. They went through the hatch into their capsule.

"Thanks for all your help!" said Alice.

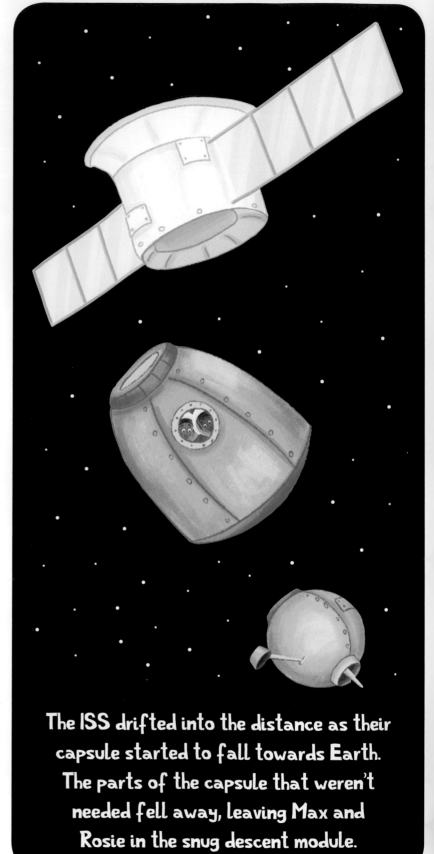

The ISS drifted into the distance as their capsule started to fall towards Earth. The parts of the capsule that weren't needed fell away, leaving Max and Rosie in the snug descent module.

Soon they were plummeting down through Earth's atmosphere. The outside of the module blazed red-hot. "I'm glad we're safely in here," said Rosie.

At last, the parachute opened with a **whoosh.**

"Wheeee!"

Rosie and Max shouted.

They landed in a grassy field with a...

...BUMP,
BUMP,
THUD!

Rosie pulled herself out of the little hatch, then helped
Max haul himself out. "Now I miss zero-gravity," she giggled.

A crowd of scientists was waiting for them where they landed.
"Well done Rosie and Max!" they cheered. "How was space?"
Rosie and Max looked at each other and grinned.

"It was **OUT OF THIS WORLD!**" they said together.

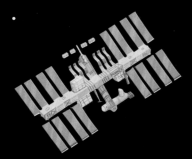

The science behind the story...

The International Space Station is a large laboratory floating hundreds of kilometres above the Earth. It's made up of lots of different pieces, or modules, attached to a long metal backbone.

Scientists visit for six months at a time to do experiments and find out how things work in space. They train for years to learn how to navigate and use complex equipment. Training even includes swimming in a pool with a life-size model of the Space Station. The pressure of the water helps astronauts practise repairing the Station in conditions that are almost like zero-gravity.

Scientists travel to the Station in a rocket called a Soyuz. They sit in a small capsule on top of several huge engines and fuel tanks. Most of the fuel is used in the first few seconds of take-off, so the rocket is programmed to let go of the empty tanks, which fall back to Earth.

Life in the Space Station is much like on Earth, except for the zero-gravity conditions. Scientists sleep, eat, exercise and do experiments, as well as play games, watch films and have fun!